STUART RO

The Wild Flowers
of Dorset

LINE DRAWINGS BY LYS DE BRAY

The Dovecote Press

First published in 1984 by The Dovecote Press Ltd
Stanbridge, Wimborne, Dorset

ISBN 0 946159 19 X

Text & photographs © Stuart Roberts 1984
Line drawings © Lys de Bray 1984

Designed by Humphrey Stone
Text printed by Biddles Ltd, Guildford, Surrey
Colour plates printed by Print Production Ltd, Poole, Dorset
Bound by the Newdigate Press Ltd, Dorking, Surrey

Contents

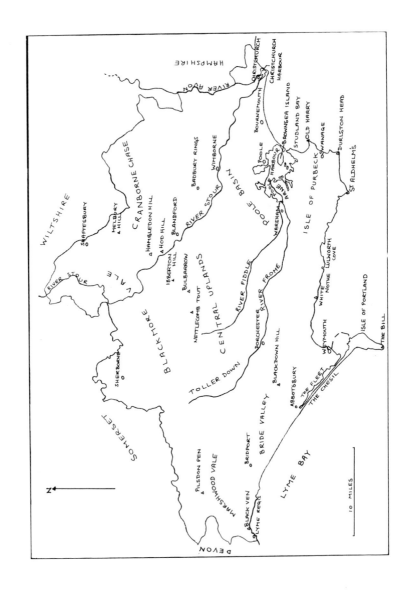

Acknowledgements

I should like to take this opportunity to thank the many people who have been instrumental in the compilation of this guide, and I hope I may be forgiven for singling out a few for special mention. I am indebted to Peter Hatherley who has been particularly helpful both as an advisor and as a knowledgeable field companion, and to Sheila Gowers at the Dorset Environmental Records Centre in Dorchester who has furnished me with vital information and a number of difficult literature sources. My colleagues at school have patiently withstood being bombarded with sheets of manuscript and boxes of slides for appraisal and their assistance and encouragement are gratefully acknowledged. I also owe thanks to the many boys who have cheerfully lugged photographic equipment into some of the county's less accessible sites and who have forced me to make scientific observations and points as brief and as clear as possible. Last but by no means least, a special word must be reserved for my two beautiful walking companions, who have been with me throughout the project from conception to completion, and to them this book is dedicated.

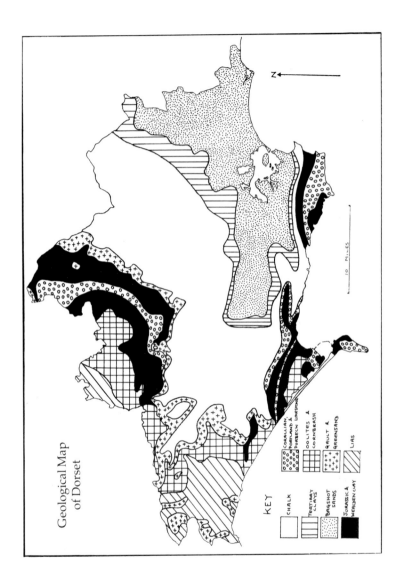

Geological Map
of Dorset

KEY

CHALK
TERTIARY CLAYS
BAGSHOT SANDS
JURASSIC & WEALDEN CLAY

CORALLIAN, PORTLAND & PURBECK LIMESTONE
OOLITES & CORNBRASH
GAULT & GREENSAND
LIAS

N

10 MILES

Introduction

Geology

Dorset has been well researched geologically as it represents a microcosm of all the geological formations present in South Eastern Britain. As many plants are limited to areas with particular soil types and the vegetation broadly mirrors the nature of the underlying geological strata, an understanding of the rock formations should give an immediate clue as to the likely flora in any given locality.

The key to the geology of Dorset is the position of the chalk. These deposits form a south western extension of the chalky Wiltshire uplands of the Salisbury Plain. They enter the county on a broad front in the Cranborne Chase before sweeping further west to form the county's central massif. A northerly spur of chalk stretches to Winyards Gap along Toller Down and a narrower and much longer eastward extension wends its sinuous way across Purbeck to Old Harry.

In the extreme east of the county, in the land bordering Poole Harbour and the lower Frome valley, tertiary deposits of Bagshot sands may be found. It is on their thin, nutrient poor soils that heathland communities can readily establish themselves. Between the Bagshot sands and the chalk, runs a band of heavy London clay which is seldom more than a few miles wide. This band is somewhat broader in the north of the region than on Purbeck, and tends to support neutral to slightly calcareous grasslands as its typical vegetation.

To the west and north of the main chalk outcrops runs a narrow band of greensand, and this interface is most apparent just below the chalk escarpment. Here the ground is sodden with water that has drained through the chalk and then met an impervious layer of water resistant clay.

Blackmore Vale is traversed by interspersed bands of Kimmeridge and Oxford clays and calcareous Corallian limestone

9

A chequered pattern of hedges criss-crosses the Blackmore Vale near Batcombe.

and cornbrash deposits, whilst the far west has a complex assortment of lias and overtopping sandstone formations.

Immediately to the south of the main body of the chalk, in a region forming the drainage of the River Wey, may be found an area of alternating clays and limestones with a small outcrop of cornbrash immediately adjacent to the northern end of the Fleet. The mighty Chesil Bank, which shelters the Fleet from the sea is the only link between the mainland and the Isle of Portland – an island constructed out of a virtually solid block of limestone on a clay base.

The Isle of Purbeck is crossed by successive narrow bands of deposits ranging from Kimmeridge clays to Bagshot sands. The coastal clay is surrounded by limestones which form the southern Purbeck plateau and the impressive cliffs both to east and west. The central valley of Wealden clay abuts the ridge of chalk that is so dramatically punctuated by Corfe Castle, whilst to the north of the chalk the tertiary sands of the Poole Basin and their fringing clays may be found.

The great geological diversity noted within the county has ensured that Dorset is blessed with one of the richest and most varied floras of any county in England.

Climate

Climatic factors have long been recognised as important in affecting the distribution of many species of plants, but the absolute values of rainfall, humidity and temperature are considerably less important than the trends shown across the county as a whole. Professor Ronald Good's *Handbook* contains a detailed discussion of these factors and has provided the backbone for this brief synopsis, his account should be consulted by anyone wishing to learn a more complete story.

Rainfall is highest on the uplands of the county in a rough line extending from Pilsdon Pen, along the chalk escarpment to Melbury Hill, just south of Shaftesbury, with values decreasing in every direction. The areas with the lowest rainfall are the coastal fringes and in particular Portland and Weymouth.

Closely allied to rainfall, but not strictly dependent upon it, are the values for atmospheric humidity. The measurement of humidity requires more elaborate instrumentation than that

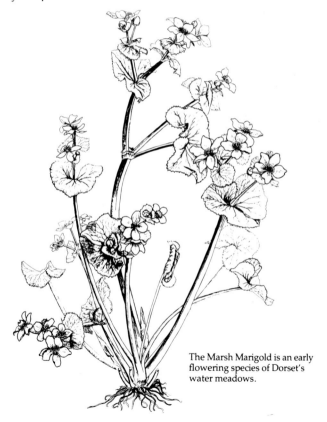

The Marsh Marigold is an early flowering species of Dorset's water meadows.

required for investigating temperature and rainfall and the picture for the county as a whole is less well understood, as are its effects upon the flora. The coastal regions appear to have the highest humidity readings and these diminish inland throughout the year, and it is significant that the differences between coastal and inland stations are most pronounced during the spring and early summer growing seasons.

Within an area the size of Dorset the variations in temperature between different regions are only relatively small but they may still have a considerable bearing on the distributions of many species. The coastal strip is practically frost free and this enables frost-intolerant species to succeed and flourish. The sea's influence is not confined to the cliff faces and coastal margins alone, and will still affect the composition of the vegetation across a zone stretching several miles inland. This sub-maritime region is typified by cooler summers and warmer winters than those encountered in the northern corners of the county.

In broad terms, Dorset can be divided into four climatic regions: a wetter and warmer west, a warmer and more humid south, a warm and dry east and a dry and cool north.

Certain species are at the climatic limits of their ranges in Dorset and these include some rare or local species. The Dorset Heath falls into this category; a member of the Lusitanian element of the British flora, it grows well on the scrubby coastal heaths of western France and on the Cornish peninsular. The most northerly stations of this species are on the heaths to the south of Poole harbour, and it is limited by temperature from growing on the heathlands of Surrey and Hampshire. Conversely, Dorset is at the southern limits of the ranges of other species, most notably the Marsh Gentian and the shingle dwelling Sea Pea. These northern species grow well in southern Britain but they suffer severely from competition from more aggressive types; types which are unable to flourish in the colder north.

Commoner species may display a 'gradient' type of distribution whereby they are more plentiful in some regions than in others. The direction of the gradient depends largely on which climatic factor is involved, and results in a decrease in the number of suitable niches along the line of the gradient. One such group of plants which includes the Primrose, the Yellow

Archangel and a number of woodland ferns is more plentiful in regions with higher rainfall and becomes increasingly scarce towards the drier east, with the Primrose confined to woodlands in these regions.

Those plants which are limited by temperature show a distinct south-north gradient and include such typically sub-maritime species as the aromatic umbellifer Alexanders and the beautiful but deadly Henbane, which are seldom found more than a few miles from the sea.

It is often extremely difficult to assess to what degree a particular species may be limited by the influences of the climate, especially if the species under consideration is either scarce or of disjunct distribution. As information concerning the more detailed distribution of plants becomes available, and the understanding broadens as to how relative humidity and vapour pressure combine with temperature and rainfall to affect the growth of plants, it is likely that more species will prove to be restricted primarily by climatic forces.

Land Use

In any survey of land use it is important to look not only at the situation as it is today, but also back into the past and attempt to understand how the countryside and its landscape have been shaped over the centuries.

Dorset is almost entirely a rural county and the principal use of the land has been in an agricultural capacity, with only the Poole-Bournemouth conurbation forming a major metropolitan development. The nature of agricultural usage of land is dependant largely on the prevailing soil types: on the chalk uplands, a mixture of downland sheep, cattle and arable may be found, whilst on the wetter clays of Marshwood and Blackmore and in the loamy valleys of the larger rivers, dairy farming has long been the most significant form of land use. The poor quality of the heathland soils of the Poole Basin has meant that they have never been of major value in farming, even during times of national emergency, such as the Napoleonic wars.

Changes in agricultural practice over the last five hundred years have led to significant changes of land use which must have affected the native flora considerably in consequence. The division and enclosure of village fields began as early as the reign of Henry VIII and continued to gain momentum until the first half of the nineteenth century, by which time most parish lands had been enclosed. The many miles of hedges that had to be laid in order to comply with acts of Parliament are a living testimony to the work of the enclosure commissioners and their sponsors. The most notable exception to this general trend towards enclosure was the Isle of Portland which retains an open field structure to this day.

With the increase in mechanisation of farming in the twentieth century, the tendency has been for some estates to remove hedges and make their fields larger. This has had a significant effect on the distribution of many hedgerow plants, and just as importantly, on the multitude of animals which depend on them.

The chalk uplands have traditionally been an area devoted to the grazing of vast flocks of sheep and this grazing led to the development of short sward chalk grassland communities

The Greater Butterfly Orchid

to the benefit of many of the smaller herbs typical of such habitats. The moves in the latter part of the eighteenth century by some large landowners, most notably the Pitt-Rivers family and Lord Portman, to convert upland sheep walk into productive arable started a swing away from the intensive sheep farming hitherto practised. Much of the chalk between Dorchester and Blandford coming under the plough during this period.

The development of specially selected grass seeds, the widespread introduction of cattle and the need for higher productivity have led to the further reduction in the acreage of 'unimproved' downland within the county; in certain areas, only those places which are either too steep or too expensive to plough have been left as a reminder of what was once the typical downland vegetation.

The acid heathland soils have supported little in the way of livestock and have been generally unproductive agriculturally, although the cropping of furze and the cutting of peat for fuel has helped maintain the structure of the heathland communities, but in the present century large tracts of previously desolate heath have become immersed in an enveloping sea of alien conifers in a bid by commercial forces to extract a livelihood from the poor soils. The expansion of Bournemouth has swallowed up acre after acre of heath and the few remaining areas are now isolated from one another, often by several miles – further than the flight of a pollinating insect.

The quantity of deciduous woodland in the county has diminished over the centuries as the need for woodland products has gradually declined. The medieval wood was the source of two major products: timber (*meremium*) from the standard Oak or Ash trees, and wood, or underwood (*subboscus*) from the self-regenerating hazel coppice. The nobility used the woods, especially those of the Cranborne Chase for the pleasures of the hunt whilst their tenant farmers often had rights to feed their livestock in their Lords' wood, and so the maintenance and preservation of woodland was in everyone's interest. Today few woods are still coppiced, a regime important to the continued survival of several of the smaller, less shade tolerant herbs, but woodland does still have its uses, most notably now as a covert for pheasant and so the continued preservation of our woodlands at the moment seems assured.

The hurdle-maker at work. The coppicing of woodland is vital to the survival of the smaller, less shade tolerant herbs.

The composition of the native flora readily reflects the patterns of land usage, and the decline of many of the rarer species within the county highlights the need for continuous careful management of our precious land resources.

Dorset Botanists

An account of the plant life in Dorset should pay some tribute to the work of the many botanists whose labours have gradually built up the considerable fund of knowledge available to us today. P. W. Carter has written a detailed historical account of the botanical exploration of the county which was published in the *Proceedings of the Dorset Natural History and Archaeological Society (Proc. D.N.H.A.S.)* and on which I have drawn heavily. This paper should be read by anyone interested in learning the full story, as there is space here to mention only the more notable figures.

Early botany was an observational exercise rather than the experimental science it is today. This is because many 'botanists' were herbalists or apothecaries and needed to know only the various stations in which the plants vital to their trade could be found and collected. In the sixteenth and seventeenth century Herbals, Dorset plants achieve several mentions, most notably from William Turner, the 'Father of English Botany' and later Matthias L'obel, James I's Flemish physician who mentioned both the Portland Spurge and the Stalked Scurvy Grass in his writings.

The first phase of the discovery of the flora continued into the eighteenth century, when sufficient information was being gathered to start amalgamating plant lists to form county floras. Prominent amongst the first of these compilations of Dorset plants was that of Richard Pulteney, the Leicester born and Edinburgh educated physician who contributed to the 1799 edition of Hutchins' *History of Dorset* what was described by a contemporary as 'one of the most valuable provincial catalogues published in England,' and included many local or rare plants some of which, like the Water Violet (*Hottonia palustris*) are today no longer found within the county

Amongst nineteenth century botanists, the Weymouth pharmacist Henry Groves deserves mention. He contributed considerably to the knowledge of the coastal flora, particularly to the region between Lulworth and Portland, before emigrating to Florence and turning his attention to the botany of Italy and the compilation of a massive personal herbarium.

In the latter part of the nineteenth century the work in the county centred upon John Clavell Mansel-Pleydell's *Flora of Dorset* which was first published in 1874 with a second edition appearing in 1895. Mansel-Pleydell collected together all the earlier known records and added to these a great number of his own and of his many correspondents, amongst whom he numbered Sir William Hooker and H. C. Watson, the leading professional botanists of their day.

It is not possible to give any specific date to mark the transition from mere accumulation of plant records to a more modern ecological approach. Professor Ronald Good using this approach set himself the task of collating the information which had been collected over the years and attempting to explain why plants grew in particular districts and associations.

Good has shown that most plants have discontinuous distributions within the county, and he suggested that a combination of climatic and edaphic factors may be responsible for affecting these distributions. Good's major contribution to the botany of the county was published by the D.N.H.A.S. in 1948 and entitled *A Geographical Handbook of the Dorset Flora*, and includes chapters on geology, climate and soils.

Good's colossal work is today being re-appraised by researchers using records from Furzebrook research station, and this undertaking will take the rest of the decade to complete. There is now a repository for information on the distributions of plants, and this is held by the Dorset Environmental Records Centre whose office is in the County Museum, and welcomes any records from amateur and professional botanists alike.

Much pleasure can still be derived in finding out something new about the rich heritage of the Dorset flora of which we are but the trustees. We should strive to pass on unspoilt this heritage to those who come after us.

Conservation

The subject of conservation is an emotive one today, with the very mention of the word sending people rushing to their respective corners and donning their gloves in defence of their actual or perceived interests. It is hoped that both a balanced look at the situation and a preparedness of interested parties to discuss the issues will ultimately enable realistic and sensible policies to be adopted.

Facets of progress which give cause for particular concern are those which require entire areas of countryside to undergo a radical change of use. Prominent here are the pressures on land caused by the building developer and by the modern methods used in commercial forestry and intensive farming. It must be hoped that a greater awareness of the need to preserve selected sites in a natural condition will also enable such developments as are necessary to have the minimum possible impact on the environment.

Today there is a greater need for farmers to obtain the maximum benefit from their land to make it as profitable as possible. New machinery and techniques have enabled many acres of once marginal land to be brought under the plough and also to extract greater yields from land already so used.

Hedges have been removed to increase the size of fields, but

Scentless Mayweed (Matricaria maritima). The familiar Mayweed is an abundant colonist of field margins.

in regions where there is little natural woodland, hedgerows become important refuges for woodland species. The widespread use of herbicides has reduced the populations of arable weed species to a dangerously low level, of great concern here is the beautiful Corn Cockle, now almost totally eradicated from Dorset. Far more serious is the leaching of farm chemicals and fertilizers into the drainage and water systems, encouraging algal growth and upsetting the balance in the waterways.

Dorset's severely threatened heathland is now reduced to a mere 14% of its 1765 level and it is still under enormous pressure. Afforestation of heathland has seen many acres of the Poole Basin swamped with cash crop conifers. This planting of monocultures of alien species is preceded by deep ploughing to bring nutrients from the lower horizons of the podsol soils to the surface and thereby to be more readily available for uptake. In a natural system, these nutrients are returned to the soil when the trees die, but in commercial forestry, the nutrients are absorbed into the trees and then removed for good, leaving a depleted soil behind them.

Over the last decade, pressure groups (both official and unofficial) have sought to bring legal safeguards to protect the countryside. These efforts culminated in the passing in 1981 of a new Wildlife and Countryside Act. The 1981 Act has caused considerable upheaval as it has proved difficult to implement fairly. Government branches find themselves at loggerheads with one another, as do farmers and conservationists, all of whom have interests in the land. For the most part the Act seeks to protect habitats and their constituent species but it is unwieldy and the general public is still largely unaware of its implications.

The Act gives special protection to a number of species and prohibits the picking, uprooting or destruction of these plants in their habitats and forbids the sale of the plants or their seeds if they are from native British stock. The Portland Rock Sea Lavender (*Limonium recurvum*) and the Early Spider Orchid (*Ophrys sphegodes*) have this special protection, as do the Lizard Orchid, Purple Spurge and the Wild Gladiolus which may already have been lost to the county.

It is not only the rarest of plants which receive attention, but commoner species are also the concern of the Act. It is now illegal to uproot intentionally (except on one's own land) any wild plant without permission. This is designed to give protection to such familiar plants as the Primrose and the Cowslip from wholesale removal by 'Plant Lovers'.

The legislators make no attempt whatsoever to stop the picking of wild flowers and fruits (except those on the specially protected list) but they hope that the public will refrain from collecting on Nature Reserves and leave the plants for others to enjoy. The Act lays a clear duty on local Education Authorities to bring the legislation to the attention of schoolchildren. It is to be hoped that this duty is taken seriously, for if any legislation is to be effective it needs to be understood by all members of the community. This educational work is backed up by the museums and the T.V. companies, whose wildlife programmes always attract attention, and stimulate widespread critical acclaim.

The enthusiasm generated in the natural world over the last decade has resulted in many people becoming interested in or joining national or local organisations involved in conservation. Apart from the National Nature Reserves, (administered and wardened by the Government's official conservation body the

N.C.C.) reserves are also maintained by voluntarily funded organisations such as the R.S.P.B. (with a heathland reserve at Arne, and a wetland site in Weymouth). Locally the Dorset Naturalist's Trust (DNT) deals with a number of reserves which range from the minute (Kilwood — ½ acre) to the imposing (Brownsea Island — 250 acres) and also runs field meetings and lectures for its members.

Satisfactory compromises can, and must be made if we are to produce all we need in the way of food, timber and houses and yet still maintain the countryside so that it, and all the treasures it has to offer can continue to be enjoyed by the generations that are yet to come.

Identification and Further Reading

The greatest joys of field botany as an exercise are that it can be enjoyed by virtually anyone, whatever their age and in almost any locality with a minimum of initial financial outlay on equipment. The only immediate musts are for suitable clothing, footwear and a field guide although to these, the more serious observer may add a notebook, a pencil and a x10 hand lens.

The selection of all the items of equipment is very much a matter of personal preference, but the choice of a field guide undoubtedly causes the most headaches. It is a task that is becoming increasingly difficult year by year as the number of splendid subject related books multiplies. I have always worked from several guides simultaneously and found that they complement one another excellently. Other people may find other guides work better for them, but these are my particular favourites, based on a number of seasons' field work:

The Concise Flora of the British Isles in Colour by the Rev. W. Keble Martin. – This book has first rate colour illustrations but is rather thin on text and a shade bulky for easy field use.

The Wild Flowers of Britain and Northern Europe (Collins Guide series) by Fitter, Fitter & Blamey. – Small and compact but again with scanty text and many non-British species illustrated.

Flora of the British Isles (2nd edition) Clapham, Tutin & Warburg. The botanists' bible, and a must for all serious planthunters; this volume is both heavy and expensive but it does describe every species in detail. The few illustrations it does contain are not of whole plants. There is a cheaper *Excursion Flora* by the same authors which, although giving comprehensive identification keys does not give elaborate detail on scarce or rare species.

Anyone interested in the more detailed study of the flora would probably wish to form a back up library of reference books. There are several titles in the Collins 'New Naturalist' series on botanical topics, and these are all to be recommended, as is the quite excellent Peter Lowe publication:

Wild Flowers – Their Habitats in Britain and Northern Europe, edited by Geoffrey Halliday and Adrian Malloch.

This book covers the vegetation types found in Europe, and describes the associations and assemblages of plants in a variety of habitats, and is beautifully illustrated with colour photos and drawings.

On a local basis, the only Dorset Floras that have been produced are long out of print and are now hard to track down and expensive.

The Flora of Dorset by J. C. Mansel-Pleydell was printed at the end of the last century and really only amounts to a glorified species list with type localities. Of more recent vintage is Professor Ronald Good's *Geographical Handbook of the Dorset Flora* which contains, in addition to the usual species list, important chapters on ecology and distributions. Although this book is scarce, it is worth searching for, but it does not make particularly light reading for any but the more dedicated student.

My strongest advice therefore, is to choose something that suits both the individual needs and pocket of the user. A small portable guide being the ideal, as it enables the botanist to take the book to the plant, and thereby leave the specimen in its habitat, to continue growing unmolested. This approach should prevent undue pressure on sensitive species and yet still enable the beholder to enjoy the pleasure of successfully identifying the specimen in question.

The Habitats

Heathland

Heathland constitutes what is probably Dorset's most distinctive habitat type, and in historical times it stretched virtually unbroken across the New Forest in neighbouring Hampshire, over what is now Bournemouth, around Poole Harbour and then as far west as the village of Bockhampton, not three miles from the centre of Dorchester. This expanse of heath running inland from Wareham between the Rivers Frome and Piddle formed what Thomas Hardy described as the 'vast tract of unenclosed wild known as Egdon Heath' – one of his major sources of inspiration.

Heathland has developed on the Tertiary gravels and sands found predominantly in the Poole Basin. The soils are deficient in nutrients, these being leached out by rain and deposited in an 'iron pan' several feet below the surface. Heathland podsol soils tend to be highly acidic in nature and thereby support a range of calcifuge plants.

Dry heathland is dominated by members of the Heather family, of which the pale-flowered Ling is the most abundant; this is frequently found alongside the richer purple of the Bell Heather. The flowers of these species are particularly attractive to honey bees, and the sight of hives placed on the heath in August must have been a familiar one to our forefathers. These two species are joined by a third, the Dorset Heath, on certain heaths to the south of Poole Harbour. This national rarity may be found in some abundance with its reddish purple flower heads making a fine show in the late summer.

The nutlike aroma of the Gorse's golden flowers is a familiar scent on the lowland heaths. This plant may be found in bloom in any month of the year but the peak flowering time is in the early spring, it is an important feature of several of the region's heaths as it is amongst its spiny branches that the endangered

The Spiny Gorse will flower throughout the year.

Dartford Warbler may seek its nest site. The smaller furzes are also found and are of widespread occurrence, with the Dwarf Gorse generally the more abundant in the east of the region.

Amongst the typical heathland herbs are the early flowering, deep blue Milkwort and the aggressively scented parasite of heathers and furzes, the Dodder, whose blood-red threadlike stems are a common sight on many of the county's heaths, whilst Sorrels, Centaury and the sticky Wood Groundsel may be found in areas with bare or disturbed ground.

The compressed soils on heathland tracks may yield an interesting flora, with scarce Clovers and the Lesser Birdsfoot being found here, often in conjunction with the miniscule Mossy Crassula. Heath Bedstraw with its cross-shaped white flowers is common along track margins and with the four petalled Tormentil is a classic indicator of acid soils. In a few secluded heathy places the Climbing Corydalis and the Heath Lobelia may still be found, but less fortunate is the Wild Gladiolus, a majestic species that may now have been eradicated through habitat destruction.

Where the heathland drainage is impeded, the conditions favour the development of *Sphagnum* dominated bog, over

24

which a variety of impressive dragonflies wing their predatory way in search of small insects. On the soggy, nitrogen deficient lawns of moss may be found the insectivorous plants: the three species of Sundew with their basal rosettes of leaves, each covered in red, glistening, sticky glandular hairs; and the apple green leaved Pale Butterwort, each seeking to absorb nutrients from its victim in this nutrient poor environment. The shrubby Bog Myrtle has overcome the problems of living under these conditions too, and has nitrogen fixing bacteria living in association with its roots, enabling atmospheric nitrogen to be converted into nitrates ready for absorption.

The common Ling and Bell Heather are intolerant of wet ground, and are replaced there by the rose flowered Cross-Leaved Heath and the deciduous Purple Moor Grass. These species may be joined by the yellow-orange flowered Bog Asphodel and the highly variable Heath Spotted Orchid, whose flowers may range from practically white to a rich purple, with the lower tip dotted or streaked with a darker colour. On a few boggy heaths, the rich blue trumpets of the Marsh Gentian can

On the compressed verges of tracks, on acid soils, the Rough Clover *(Trifolium scabrum)* grows amongst colonizing mosses.

still be seen brightening the scene in late August or September.

Small heathland pools may boast White Waterlilies, Bogbean and occasionally Quillwort — an aquatic non-flowering relative of the ferns, whilst the fringes of the pool may be marked by a belt of small trees, most notably Birch and Sallow, and sometimes the Alder Buckthorn. In addition to the widespread Bracken, damp, shady areas of Studland Heath may have the Royal Fern, a truly noble species, much reduced in the past through over-collecting by Victorian fern hunters.

Invasive non-native plants are spreading on some heaths to the detriment of the local flora. Most noticeable here are the Scots Pine, whose wind-borne seeds have led to the establishment of not inconsiderable pine woods on ungrazed heaths and also the Rhododendron whose leaves act as an impenetrable barrier to light, killing all low growing species around them.

With heathland being swallowed up yearly for housing, agriculture and forestry it is all the more significant that various conservation bodies, most notably the N.C.C., R.S.P.B. and the D.N.T. hold important areas of heath as some reminder of the times when Hardy regarded this part of Dorset as being a 'heathery world'.

Calcareous Grassland

Natural or semi-natural calcareous grassland can develop over any base-rich rock formation, and in Dorset these types are represented by the Corallian, Portland and Purbeck limestones, the broken cornbrash outcrops in north west Dorset, and also over the bulk of the widespread chalk.

The chalk deposits in the county stretch from the boundaries of neighbouring Wiltshire and Hampshire in a south-westerly direction forming the Central Upland Massif. A narrow eastward extension brushes the coast between White Nothe and Worbarrow Bay before forming the narrow, spine-like ridge of Purbeck. This ridge rejoins the sea to the north of Swanage, forming the dazzling cliffs and stacks of Old Harry and Handfast Point.

The grey rendzina soils which develop over much of the chalk are generally base-rich loams which drain easily but are capable of retaining moisture in their lower levels. Such environments tend to support species-rich assemblages of calcicolous plants.

Until comparatively recently, the chalk uplands played host to many hundreds of thousands of sheep and rabbits. The extensive grazing by these species prevented the growth of tall grassland and ensured that there was little or no invasion of the downland by woody shrubs or trees. By the mid-1970's, as the sheep population had been reduced to a fifth of its peak 1850 level, and rabbits had been decimated by the ravages of myxomatosis, many acres of grassland had given way to scrub.

Chalk grassland has also suffered at the hands of the increas-

Plentiful in both Chalk and Limestone grasslands, the Carline Thistle's *(Carlina vulgaris)* dead stems persist throughout the winter.

ing intensification of agriculture. The current economic climate demands the use of specially selected grasses in preference to the less productive natural species. As a result of this, areas of natural grassland are now often restricted to sheep, unploughable slopes and hillsides. The ramparts of many of Dorset's impressive hill forts still provide an excellent opportunity to view short turf and open-sward vegetation. Vegetation types which remain today in a similar condition to that which must have prevailed more generally two hundred years ago.

A visitor to the chalk in springtime should still find the nodding, rich yellow heads of Cowslip – each flower encased in an inflated sepal tube. Where Cowslips grow in close proximity to the woodland Primrose, a hybrid of the two species may occasionally be found. This hybrid, called a False Oxlip, has the orange spot typical of its Cowslip parent at the base of each petal which distinguishes it from the true Oxlip – a native of the boulder clay woods of East Anglia and unknown in Dorset.

Other early flowering species include two species of Milkwort, whose flowers range from white, through pink to a rich royal blue, and the Hairy Violet, notable for its soft hairy stems and leaves and flowers that decrease in size as the season progresses. Often in association with these two may be found the wind pollinated Salad Burnet, a dowdy flower indeed in comparison with its showy, insect pollinated relatives in the Rose family.

Many of the taller and more rapidly growing species of neutral grassland are intolerant of the shortage of soil phosphate and nitrate that generally accompany conditions of high base-status. Under these conditions, on more freely drained hillslopes, and encouraged by grazing, short herb communities can flourish.

27

Nitrogen fixers, such as the yellow flowered Pea family plants: Kidney Vetch, Birdsfoot Trefoil and Horseshoe Vetch favour these short turf sites, and the last named species is important locally as it is the larval foodplant of the Adonis Blue Butterfly. Amongst other yellow flowered herbs one should find the lemon coloured Hawkweed and the sulphurous Rock Rose and possibly the Field Fleawort. This species has a curious national distribution; virtually absent from the chalk of South East England, it is usually encountered on ancient earthworks in the southwest and in the Chilterns.

The activities of moles and hummock building ants favour the spread of rhizomatous perennials, particularly the Hoary Plantain and the Stemless or 'Picnic' Thistle, two species that are usually held in check by the dominant grasses.

Two of the most attractive species of chalk downland may be found in flower in late June. The first, that most delicate of Grasses, the Totter or Quaking Grass, bears flower spikes that are wafted by the merest hint of a breeze. The second is the charming Eyebright, one of a complex aggregate series of plants which has numerous regional and ecological microspecies, and is so named from the salve that was made by the herbalists from an infusion of the aerial parts.

The late summer brings into flower the densely spiny Carline Thistle, the bane of picnickers and a widespread species. The dried stems of this biennial persist right throughout the winter. The scarce Bastard Toadflax, a hemi-parasite of the Sandalwood family, displays its tiny white flowers in August and is followed into bloom by the Autumn Gentian, whose narrow purple trumpets, fringed at the mouth with a characteristic ring of hairs may occur in such abundance in suitable places as to completely carpet the ground.

Tall grassland, the typical formation on level or less well drained sites, and dominated by Brome Grass, is the home of a colourful array of summer flowering species. Most frequently encountered are the sky blue Scabious, the Ox-Eye Daisy, the Wild Carrot (the forebear of the garden vegetable), and the partly-parasitic Hayrattle. This species can produce its own sugars in its green leaves and bracts, but it needs to be attached to the roots of surrounding grasses to gain vital water and nutrients. Total parasites in the shape of the Tall and Common

Broomrapes are present too, parasitizing respectively the Greater Knapweed and a range of Clovers and Trefoils. The Broomrapes' flowering spikes emerge in June and are the only part of the plant visible above ground during the course of the year.

The undoubted jewels in the chalk downland crown are the curious and flamboyant orchids. Few sites could boast a full complement of these colourful ornaments, but in favoured localities they may grow in heartening abundance. The first species into flower is the Early Purple Orchid, whose rich purple spikes and boldly blotched leaves enliven the downs as early as April. May heralds the dawn of the orchid season proper; it is then that the insignificant but plentiful green flowered Greater Twayblade may be found, and sometimes, as at Badbury Rings, in such numbers as to be the major component of the flora on some north facing slopes.

As the sun wheels towards the solstice, the down may be a showcase for a range of pink flowered species. The first to show, the Common Spotted Orchid is the most widespread, and together with the later blooming Fragrant and Pyramidal Orchids tends to favour slightly longer grass than the previously encountered Twayblade. The Pyramidal Orchid is a member of the southern European element of our flora and shows behaviour typical of such plants. In the Mediterranean regions this plant grows and flowers in the dampness of spring, and by midsummer the foliage has died back. The uncertainties of the English winter prevent any such early activity here, and so as to ensure an adequate supply of moisture for growth in the summer, it is most usually to be found on slopes with a northern or eastern aspect.

Easily the most bizarre of the chalk-loving orchids is the Bee Orchid. A species with a widespread distribution within the county wherever there is a rich supply of bases in the soil, it is nonetheless virtually confined within those areas to niches with either a closely grazed sward or to sites where the vegetation cover is incomplete and raw chalk predominates. The resemblance of the strikingly marked lip to the body of an insect is uncanny. The flower entices male bees, making them an empty offer of sexual satisfaction. During the ensuing pseudocopulation, the hapless bee may either collect pollen from the hanging pollinia, or if it has been fooled previously, deposit the pollen

The Ox-Eye Daisy
(*Leucanthemum vulgare*) is a
widespread component of tall
grassland communities.

which it has been carrying on its back on the receptive female stigma.

Whilst the coastal and inland limestones support a largely similar flora on their red-brown rendzina soils to that found on the chalk, there are certain species which show a decided preference for, and some which are completely restricted to limestone within the county.

The early spring months of April and May bring many botanists to Purbeck in search of some of Dorset's most celebrated floral treasures. The Southern Lords and Ladies, with its small pale spadix grows in the coastal scrub and grassland to the west of Durlston Head, and the scarce annual Early Gentian is at home in open grassland in the same area. The Early Purple Orchids are plentiful and they are joined by the splendid Early Spider Orchid. Although this plant is extremely uncommon nationally, within its localized range on the Dorset coast it may be found in some numbers. It must be remembered that this gem (emblem of the Dorset Naturalist's Trust) could easily be eradicated if picked or collected illegally.

The Wild Clary, a stickily hairy blue flowered relative of the mint and the leafless Yellow Vetchling (*Lathyrus aphaca*) also adorn the Durlston grasslands and the Dwarf Tufted Centaury (now sadly reduced to subspecific status in the Flora Europaea) has a station on Purbeck in short grassland.

The summer brings out the full range of typical Downland plants and includes the yellow flowered, pungent umbellifer the Wild Parsnip. Distinct majesty is provided by the regal Woolly Headed Thistle. This tall growing species is virtually confined to the limestones of the coast and north west Dorset, and although Hod Hill boasts a small but thriving colony, it is all but absent from the chalk.

In the main, there are two physical features which draw botanists to particular localities. These are the presence of water and limestone or chalk, and we are most fortunate in Dorset to possess these commodities in plenty, and lucky too that they support such a wealth of attractive and unusual species.

Deciduous Woodland

In most habitats, woodland is the natural climax vegetation, but often these woods have been radically affected by the influence of man and his activities. There is probably no untouched primary woodland in Dorset today except perhaps small heathland Birch woods and river valley Alder Carr scrub.

It is ancient woodland; man maintained and managed but of spontaneous origin that is of major botanical interest. A map of Dorset produced in 1765 indicates the extent of woodland at that time and it is of interest that many areas dominated by trees in the mid-eighteenth century remain so today. From time immemorial man has utilised woodland for a variety of purposes. It has been a supplier of food for his livestock, the producer of timber for his buildings and hazel spars for thatching and hurdle making.

The ancient woodland art of coppicing Hazel (cutting back the poles to ground level) on a cyclical basis, whilst leaving selected tall trees, usually Ashes or Oaks, as 'Standards' has diminished but it has not totally disappeared. Woodmen can still be seen at work in the coppices bordering the Piddle valley in central southern Dorset where they remove Hazel wands for splitting and making into hurdles and wicket-gates.

Many of the deciduous woodlands in the county fall into the broad category of Oakwoods but there are certain areas where the dominant tree is Ash. This is particularly noticeable in the magnificent Ash Hanger known as Creech Great Wood on Purbeck. There is some Beech woodland too, particularly on shallow chalky soils, but Beech has also been planted as a wind-breaking screen (as at Wimborne St. Giles) and serves a second purpose as an excellent covert for game.

31

Woodland is probably the most complex of temperate habitats with four distinct vegetation levels present, namely: canopy, the shrub layer, the herb layer and the ground layer (usually composed of mosses and liverworts). It is the variety of plants within the herb layer that will primarily concern us, as there is easily the greatest floristic diversity within this niche.

Winter is a season of light on the woodland floor and as early as January the first signs of the new season may be noted. The delicate yellow lamb's tail male catkins of the coppice Hazel show in the mid-winter gloom. They make use of the fickle wind as a pollinator before the springtime flushing of leaves places another barrier between pollen producing stamens and tiny, bud-like, red crowned female flowers.

The arrow-head shaped leaves of the familiar Lords and Ladies unfurl like unravelling cigars as they thrust forcefully through the surface humus alongside the heart shaped blotchy leaves of the Lesser Celandine. In the shrub layer the corky-barked Elder is also making use of the new year light and precociously bursting into leaf.

The woodland floor is at its most colourful in the spring, for

The Polypody *(Polypodium vulgaris)* is commonly found on shady banks or as an epiphyte on oak trees.

The Cross Leaved Heath *(Erica tetralix)* replaces the Bell Heather on wetter heathland.

The Bell Heather *(Erica cinerea)* is typical of dry heath and will be found growing alongside the Ling *(Calluna vulgaris)*.

The Burnet Rose *(Rosa pimpinellifolia)* is widespread on Purbeck, and grows readily on heathland.

The Dorset Heath *(Erica ciliaris)* is plentiful within its very restricted range.

The bluish Heath Dog Violet *(Viola canina)* is not uncommon on the Poole Basin Heaths.

Plate 2   Heathland

In damper situations, the short-stemmed Lousewort *(Pedicularis sylvatica)* is regularly encountered.

The carnivorous Sundew *(Drosera intermedia)* derives its Nitrogen from its ensnared victims.

On a lawn of bog moss, the delicate Bog Pimpernel *(Anagallis tenella)* flowers in July.

The Bog Pondweed *(Potamogeton polygonifolius)* inhabits permanently wet ditches and heathland ponds.

The golden Bog Asphodel *(Narthecium ossifragum)* flowers briefly in July on wet heath.

The totally parasitic Tall Broomrape *(Orobanche elatior)* flowers in July, at the same time as its host the Greater Knapweed.

The Stemless Thistle *(Cirsium acaule)* is amongst the most obvious species in short turf.

The Hay Rattle *(Rhinanthus minor)* is a hemi-parasitic member of the Foxglove family, and derives water and nutrients from its grass host.

The Clustered Bellflower *(Campanula glomerata)* is a locally occurring species in Dorset. The wide trumpets attract foraging bees.

One of Dorset's prized botanical gems, the Early Spider Orchid *(Ophrys sphegodes)* flowers in late April and is restricted to the coastal limestone between Durlston and St Aldhelm's.

Plate 4　　　Calcareous Grassland

The Fragrant Orchid *(Gymnadenia conopsea)* is locally abundant, and although the purplish colour form is the most usual, a white variety may be found.

The rare Burnt Tip Orchid *(Orchis ustulata)* is confined to the Northern Chalk. Its overall height seldom exceeds 6 inches.

The showy Bee Orchid *(Ophrys apifera)* prefers open communities and is equally at home on chalk and limestone.

The Green-Winged Orchid *(Orchis morio)* is a variable species that is characterised by the green veining on the upper petals.

The Common Spotted Orchid *(Dactylorhiza fuchsii)* is the most abundant of the Downland orchids.

The rich golden-yellow of the Lesser Celandine (*Ranunculus ficaria*) is a familiar sight in woods and hedges.

The Primrose (*Primula vulgaris*) is probably one of the best known, and most widespread woodland herbs.

The Wood Anemone, or Wind Flower (*Anemone nemorosa*) can form a dense carpet in the early Spring woodland.

February brings the scarce Green Hellebore (*Helleborus viridis*) into flower.

The Common Violet (*Viola riviniana*) is characterised by its pale, notched spur.

Plate 6   Deciduous Woodland

Under Hazels, on chalky soils, the parasitic Toothwort *(Lathraea squamaria)* may occasionally be found.

The diminuitive Town Hall Clock *(Adoxa moschatellina)* is an indicator of ancient woodland and coppice.

In a few localities, in damp copses and thickets, the Summer Snowflake *(Leucojum aestivum)* may still be found.

The commonest woodland orchid, the Early Purple *(Orchis mascula)* flourishes under shady coppice and flowers in April and May.

The Hawthorn *(Crataegus monogyna)* red with
Autumn berries, was favoured by the hedge
carpenters for its ability to provide a stockproof
boundary rapidly.

A good crop of Sloes on the Blackthorn *(Prunus spinosa)* usually follows a warm May when the
shrub is in flower.

Roses are plentiful, climbing with aid from their
sharply thorned stems, and include the Sweet
Briar *(Rosa rubiginosa).*

The Honeysuckle *(Lonicera periclymenum)* is a
woody climber at home in hedges, woods and on
scrubby undercliffs..

Disturbed ground and hedgebanks are favoured
haunts of the bee-pollinated Black Horehound
(Ballota nigra).

Plate 8   Hedgerows

The white flowers of the Traveller's Joy *(Clematis vitalba)* will give way to fluffy heads of Old Man's Beard in the Autumn.

The only native member of the Cucumber family; the White Bryony *(Brionia dioica)* is a common hedgerow climber on the chalk.

The Bush Vetch *(Vicia sepium)* is one of the most delicate of hedgerow herbs.

The Red Campion *(Silene dioica)* is one of the select band of British species with the male and female flowers on separate plants.

The White Dead Nettle *(Lamium album)* has a peculiar distribution in Dorset and is a doubtful native.

Amphibious Bistort *(Polygonum amphibium)*. This species is equally at home either as a floating aquatic or as a streamside terrestrial.

Water meadows are the habitat of the cut-petalled Ragged Robin *(Lychnis flos-cuculi)*.

The tall Flag Iris *(Iris pseudacorus)* is a common species found in Alder Carr Woods and drainage ditches.

The Marsh Marigold or Kingcup *(Caltha palustris)* flourishes in water meadows and is early into flower.

All parts of the Hemlock Water Dropwort *(Oenanthe crocata)* are highly toxic. It is nonetheless a common and widespread species.

The majestic Great Willowherb *(Epilobium hirsutum)* may be found on the banks of many a river, stream or ditch.

Plate 10

River and Wetland

The flower spikes of the Butterbur *(Petasites hybridus)* emerge in advance of the leaves.

The Ladies' Smock *(Cardamine pratensis)* is a May-flowering inhabitant of water meadows.

Cliff and Undercliff

The Marsh Helleborine *(Epipactis palustris)* is an orchid of damp undercliffs and flowers in late June.

The Southern Marsh Orchid *(Dactylorhiza majalis ssp praetermissa)* is widespread in damp habitats and is often plentiful on undercliffs.

Although the Portland Spurge *(Euphorbia portlandica)* is common on Portland it is also found on the cliffs of Lulworth.

The lilac tinged flowers of the Stalked Scurvy Grass *(Cochlearia danica)* appear in late April and May.

The flowers of the Coltsfoot *(Tussilago farfara)* appear in advance of the leaves.

The Wild Cabbage *(Brassica oleracea)* is the ancestor of the garden vegetable and is extremely plentiful on the Purbeck Cliffs.

The Fleabane *(Puliceria dysenterica)* is a fly pollinated member of the Thistle family and is fond of heavy, moist soils.

The Spur Valerian *(Centranthus ruber)* is an introduced species which is now widely naturalised.

Plate 12   Sand Dune and Shingle Bank

The Common Storksbill *(Erodium cicutarium)* is at home on the sandy ridges of the Studland Dune complex.

The Sea Campion *(Silene maritima)* will flower for much of the summer and is plentiful on the Chesil.

The beautiful Sea Pink *(Armeria maritima)* may carpet the landward side of the Chesil in May and June.

The Shrubby Sea-Blite *(Suaeda fruticosa)* is confined in Dorset to the shingle near Smallmouth in the lee of the Chesil.

The succulent, bluish leaved Sea Kale *(Crambe maritima)* is plentiful on the shingle near Bexington.

Fruits of the fleshy-leaved maritime sub-species of the Woody Nightshade *(Solanum dulcamara)*.

The locally occurring Sea Pea *(Lathyrus japonicus)* is one of Chesil's greatest treasures.

Legumes are common on shingle; the Birdsfoot Trefoil *(Lotus corniculatus)* is one of the most plentiful.

The Yellow Horned Poppy *(Glaucium flavum)* is so named for its long curved seed pods, produced from July.

The foetid Restharrow *(Ononis repens)* once the bane of dairymen, can survive on the fine shingles near Abbotsbury.

Plate 14   Saltmarsh

A combination of purplish Sea Lavender
(*Limonium vulgare*) and Buckshorn Plantain
(*Plantago coronopus*) on grazed Saltmarsh at
Stanpit.

The Narrow-Headed Thistle (*Cirsium tenuiflorus*) is
confined to coastal habitats but is infrequent in
saltmarshes.

The English Scurvy grass (*Cochlearia anglica*) is
a plentiful species in saltmarshes and flowers in
late May and early June.

Amongst the litter of beached material on the
upper Marsh, the fleshy Celery-leaved Crowfoot
(*Ranunculus sceleratus*) may be found.

The downy-leaved, pale flowered Marsh Mallow
(*Althaea officinalis*) is found only on the upper
reaches of the marsh.

The Sea Aster *(Aster tripolium)* has fleshy leaves to help conserve water in its salt laden environment.

Mud-filled hollows may be home for the Saltmarsh Water Crowfoot *(Ranunculus baudottii)*.

Weeds and Aliens

The beautiful Corn Cockle *(Agrostemma githago)* has suffered as the quality and purity of cereal seed has improved.

There can be few finer sights to the botanist than a field full of Poppies *(Papuver rhoeas)*.

Plate 16   Weeds and Aliens

The red petals of the Scarlet Pimpernel (*Anagallis arvensis*) will close the moment the sun goes in.

The flower heads of the Goatsbeard (*Tragopogon pratensis*) shut around mid-day and gave rise to the country name "Johnny-go-to-bed-at-Noon".

The Germander Speedwell (*Veronica chamaedrys*) is characterised by a line of hairs on each side of its stems.

The Sainfoin (*Onobrychis viciifolia*) is no longer planted as a fodder crop, but it persists in the wild near its former strongholds.

The Common Mallow (*Malva sylvestris*) has well defined "honey guides" on its petals to guide incoming insects to its nectaries.

A small fly visiting the flowers of Burdock (*Arctium minus*). The hooked involucral bristles are visible supporting the flowers.

alongside the green flowered Mercury and the delicate Moschatel or Town Hall Clock grows the Primrose, the harbinger of spring. In order to flourish, Primroses require an adequate supply of water, and whilst it is a widespread inhabitant of the county's woods it is only regularly encountered in hedgerows in the wetter west. The flowers of the Primrose are adapted for cross-pollination, an evolutionary advantage. It has two mutually dependant forms of flower. One, named the 'Pin-eyed' form has a long styled female stigma in the centre of the floral disc and short male stamens out of sight in the petal tube. The other form, termed 'Thrum-eyed' has the long male stamens at the top and the short female apparatus is concealed. Each can only fertilize the other form and this promotes out-breeding.

Further spring beauty is added by two related species of plant that may frequently carpet the woodland floor: the fragile white Wood Anemone or Wind Flower and its golden yellow cousin the Lesser Celandine. Small white flowers include the Wood-Sorrel, whose presence indicates either an acid soil or an acidic superficial deposit over chalk. The Barren Strawberry produces flowers which are extremely similar to those of the more familiar Wild Strawberry, but differs from it in having a notched margin to each of its five petals.

Under coppiced hazel on chalky soil one may occasionally come across the parasitic Toothwort. The white heads containing the purplish flowers of this bizarre species are the only visible aerial parts; the remainder of the plant is attached to its unfortunate host which supplies it with both water and foodstuffs.

May is undoubtedly Bluebell time (Wild Hyacinths to my Caledonian forebears) and the sight and smell of a woodland full of these plants is breathtaking. The Bluebell will photosynthesize a year's supply of food in the winter and early spring before bursting into hazy blue bloom. The scented, tubular flowers are popular with foraging bees whose visual perception is particularly acute at the blue end of the spectrum. The fragrance given off by Ramsons is less pleasing to many. This wild garlic may dominate areas of certain woods (as it does in parts of the Chase and again in Creech Great Wood) but its star shaped white flowers more than compensate for the overpowering aroma of its bruised leaves.

Two other woodland species deserve mention here. One is the Yellow Archangel – Britain's only yellow Dead Nettle, which is extremely uncommon in the south and east of the county (namely the warmer and drier regions) but plentiful further west. The other is the Wood Sanicle, an umbellifer blessed with palmately lobed leaves (unusual in this family) and hooked, animal dispersed fruits.

The shade tolerant Stinking Iris has an unusual distribution in Dorset. The glossy green persistent leaves, unobtrusive flowers, and striking orange seeds, are a familiar sight in woods and thickets inland but in the coastal regions it is also found in grassland.

Ferns too are a common sight in woodland with the Buckler Ferns and Bracken being the most obvious. Hart's Tongue Fern is often abundant as is the Polypody either on acid soils or growing as an epiphyte on ancient oaks.

With the canopy trees bursting into leaf in May the woodland floor falls into a mysterious humid summer twilight and the spring flowers start dying back to their replenished storage organs be they corm, rhizome or bulb.

Few species flower in the summer months and those that do tend to be of a pale hue. For instance the diminutive Enchanter's Nightshade (not really a Nightshade but a small woodland Willowherb) and the yellow Wood Avens. Both species attract flies as pollinators and have hooked fruits for dispersal in the autumn. The majestic Nettle-leaved Bellflower is found in some woods in the centre of the county and also (in some abundance) on Purbeck.

No description of woodland would be complete without mention of its orchids, and Beech woods boast a fine collection. Characteristic species include the scarce Fly Orchid, a slender relative of the more flamboyant Bee Orchids of chalk downland. Present too is the Large White Helleborine whose white petals never open fully to reveal the bright orange spot at their bases. The most unusual of all the woodland orchids is the Bird's Nest Orchid, a parasite on leaf-rotting fungi. Often termed a saprophyte it has no innate ability to rot vegetation itself and needs the services of a fungus to assist it. It seems strange that a higher plant should stoop to parasitizing a lowly fungus but it must be remembered that all orchids require fungal aid for several years after germination. Of the commoner species it is only the Bird's Nest Orchid which never acquires chlorophyll to make its own sugars.

Climbers drape themselves over trees and shrubs alike and Ivy is amongst the most obvious. The Ivy flowers in October and November and is attractive to late-flying insects. Even in the absence of wasps (a frequent visitor) pollinating flies will ensure the production of viable seeds the following spring. The moth-enticing Honeysuckle is another favourite, its heady perfume and nectar filled trumpets being at their best in early autumn evenings.

In the valleys of the larger rivers, under a canopy of Alder and shrubby Sallows and Guelder Rose, Carr vegetation can develop. Tussocky sedges grow readily in the waterlogged soils and they are usually accompanied by Cornfrey and Yellow Flag Iris, and in one well documented south Dorset locality, amongst a tangle of nettles, the poisonous but beautiful blue Monkshood.

The powerfully scented Bluebells are in full flower in May

Hedgerows

With the widespread introduction of hedge-bound enclosures to Dorset starting in the sixteenth century the county has a long tradition of hedging and hedgerow management. Hedges provide not only a convenient dividing line between the properties of neighbouring farmers or between various crops on the same farm but also an interlinked network of thicket and cover for wildlife and a perfect refuge for many woodland plants: be they herb, rambler, shrub or tree.

The shrubs present in a hedgerow may give an indication as to the approximate age of a hedge. It has been calculated that for every hundred years of age, the hedge will gain one new species of shrub. Therefore Saxon or Norman parish boundary hedges may have up to ten species of shrub per thirty metre section, whereas Elizabethan enclosure hedges may have only four or five and late eighteenth century hedges may have as few as two species. This position can occasionally be complicated if the hedge in question is a linear remnant of a species rich wood, long since gone to the axe.

The shrub species flower in a succession of foamy creams and whites throughout the spring. Blackthorn is the first to show, with flowers produced in late March and followed in turn by Wild Cherry, Wayfaring Tree, Hawthorn, Elder and Privet. Other shrubs may be more in evidence at other times of the year – the Dog Rose whose pale flowers epitomise summer, the Spindle, whose lurid carmine and orange berries typify autumn,

The white Field Rose *(Rosa arvensis)*.

The Lords and Ladies is the most typical of hedgerow herbs.

and the blood red twigs of the Dogwood which brighten the scene in winter. Other species may include Holly, Guelder Rose, Willow, Hazel and the spiky Butcher's Broom which bears its waxy red berries on its green flattened leaf-like stems. Oak and Ash also occur, and here and there may be observed the skeletons of dead Elms, the hedgerow population of which has all but been extinguished by the ravages of Dutch Elm disease.

The smaller herbs typical of hedgerows frequently include the early flowering woodland species of Bluebell, Mercury, Celandine, Primrose, and Lords and Ladies; whilst a month later the hedgerow may be awash with colour. The bright pink of the Red Campion, a plant particularly abundant in the west of the county contrasting with the golden yellow of Buttercups, the deeply dissected white of the Greater Stitchwort and the pungent Hedge Garlic. The presence of a rabbit warren under a hedge may be indicated by the occurrence of Stinging Nettles. Nettles demand a ready supply of soil nitrates and phosphates to grow, and in

37

The hedgerow acts as a living
framework for the climbing
Honeysuckle.

some regions, most notably on the chalk (where these substances are scarce), rabbit droppings and bones provide a viable alternative source of these essential nutrients.

A variety of tall umbellifers line the spring and summer hedgerows, each topped with a flattened, powerfully scented flower head which attracts a range of pollinating flies and beetles. In sub-maritime regions, never much more than a few miles from the influence of the sea, the greenish flowered, aromatic Alexanders may be found flowering as early as March, whilst inland, the first and frequently the dominant member of the hedgerow flora is the white flowered Cow Parsley. After the passage of May, the smaller Rough Chervil with its purple-blotched stems comes into its own. This species is in turn followed by the broader heads of the Hogweed whose dried and hollow stems remain like gaunt sentinels in the autumn and winter hedgerow.

The hedgerow provides a living framework over which many ramblers and climbers drape themselves, from the delicate Bush and Tufted Vetches and the Yellow Meadow Vetchling to the more robust hooked Goosegrass and the clockwise twining stems of the Black Bryony, whose waxy scarlet berries hang like necklaces in the autumn time. Most of the climbers are at their most obvious at the end of the summer when they are either in flower, like the nectar rich Ivy, or in fruit when bedecked with an array of colourful fruits or berries. The Wild Hop, the red-berried Woody Nightshade, the thickets of Brambles whose sweet, juicy fruits are attractive to birds, wasps and September flying butterflies such as the Comma, and the festoons of fluffy Old Man's Beard which hangs from the hedgerows in chalky regions are all of widespread occurrence within the county.

Traditional hedge laying techniques involving cutting the hedge with specially shaped bill-hooks and shaping it around fixed dead wood poles have largely been superseded by mechanical hedge trimmers which flail or cut the hedges indiscriminately seldom leaving oak, ash or maple to grow into the tall trees once typical of the hedgerow scene.

A far greater threat to hedgerow communities is posed by the modern farming methods practised on some farms which involves the wholesale removal of hedges and the re-establishment of huge fields with the boundaries marked by fencing. It is to be hoped that common sense will ultimately prevail and that it is remembered that the obvious immediate benefits to be gained from hedge removal must be offset against the possible adverse long term effects which may follow the upsetting of the local balance of nature.

River and Wetland

As Dorset possesses only a small handful of still water lakes, the majority of aquatic vegetation is of necessity associated with the river systems, their accompanying water meadows, and drainage ditches.

Flowing water provides an uncertain environment in which to grow, and under these precarious circumstances the only major colonists are those plants that can both root firmly and present little resistance to the passage of water. The puzzling Water Crowfoot series, a closely allied group of white flowered Water Buttercups, and two species of Water Dropwort, toxic relatives of

The Bindweed *(Calystegia sepium)* is not strictly aquatic, but it is common on the banks of streams and is an abundant climber in such habitats.

(Opposite): Emergent and floating aquatic vegetation in the Stour below Tarrant Crawford Bridge.

the hedgerow Cow Parsley, provide the only real answer to the problems posed by turbulent flow. The leaves are submerged, finely dissected and easily wafted by water currents without being damaged or bruised. The Water Dropworts are largely confined to the larger rivers but the Water Crowfoot may be found in the smaller streams such as the Tarrant, Allen and North Winterborne in addition to the larger waterways.

Nearer the banks of the river, the rate of flow is considerably reduced, and patches of slack water may occur in the lee of bank-side obstacles, bends in the river or small promontories. It is here that the perennial Arrowhead may be found, so named because of the shape of its floating leaves. Frequently in association with the Arrowhead is the Amphibious Bistort. This species is truly amphibious, and can survive happily as an aquatic or as a river-side terrestrial with the aid of modified stems and foliage. The Yellow Water Lily also favours slower water in the major streams, especially the Stour, but its distribution may be affected by widespread planting as an ornamental.

Tall, grasslike plants often dominate the river margin. The Common Reed is usually the most abundant, and it is readily identifiable at almost any time of year. Despite its habit of dying back each autumn, the dried stems will persist throughout the winter months. The leaves swivel freely on these dried stems and will appear arranged in a line on the side sheltered from the wind. In Grass species, the junction point of leaf blade and stem is protected by a small membranous flap of tissue which will provide a watertight seal. The Common Reed is the only tall grass to have this flap reduced to a characteristic fringe of delicate hairs.

In the larger rivers, the reed may be joined by the Great Reed-mace (a long time favourite with florists and often mistakenly referred to as a Bulrush), and the Sea Clubrush, a species most usually encountered in saltmarshes, but curiously at home in the slow moving Stour.

The muddy, often trampled interface between open water and adjacent land may boast a wide variety of species on its nutrient rich alluvial soils. Three hairless Water Speedwells, whose flowers may range from pale pink to a rich royal blue, and the pale blue flowered Water Forget-Me-Not are of particularly widespread occurrence and may be found lining the banks of many a river, stream or ditch.

The tall, robust Water Figwort whose strangely shaped reddish-brown flowers are highly attractive to pollinating wasps, and the spiny Teasel are both typical waterside plants. The Teasel is not confined to this habitat, as it is also found in hedges and damp undercliffs. It has paired leaves that pass right around the stem. These leaves collect rainwater and form a protective moat, which guards the flower heads from marauding nectar pilferers such as ants.

White flowered, foetid, fly-pollinated umbellifers may also clothe the river bank. The true Hemlock (cause of the untimely demise of Socrates) is characterized by a purple blotched stem and finely dissected leaves, and the equally poisonous Hemlock Water Dropwort with its deceptive celery-like foliage are the

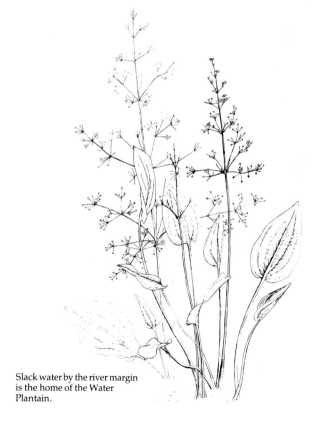

Slack water by the river margin is the home of the Water Plantain.

most frequently encountered. The latter species chokes the upper reaches of the South Winterborne to the exclusion of all other plants.

Two other locally occurring streamside species deserve mention here. The stately Meadow Rue has highly reduced petals and prominent yellow, pollen producing stamens. Although the plant is fragrant and attracts insects, it also relies on the wind for the successful transfer of pollen – an unusual feature in the buttercup family. The Butterbur can only spread by vegetative means, as every recorded plant in Dorset is male. The Butterbur's pale pink flower spikes are produced in April, and precede the leaves, which, when fully expanded, are the largest of any native British species.

In the broad vales of Frome and Stour lie many water meadow systems, a large number of which have either fallen into disrepair through neglect or have been deliberately drained and re-seeded. These meadows were vital for valley farmers and dairymen alike as what Hardy described as the 'succulent feed which the water meads supplied at the prime season of the year' enabled their livestock to be in pasture earlier than those in less favoured localities.

The first plants into bloom each year are usually the Marsh Marigolds whose clumps of golden-yellow Buttercup-like flowers dot the meadow in the early spring. These are followed by their more diminutive cousin the Lesser Spearwort and the delicate cut-petalled Ragged Robin which presents an illusion of unlikely tattiness amongst the grass stems. This species will continue flowering throughout the summer and may even persist until the later months of autumn.

The unusual Marsh Valerian is an infrequent component of the wetland flora and joins the Holly and the Stinging Nettle on the select list of species which has its male and female flowers on separate plants. More common, and certainly more obvious are the spineless Meadow Thistle and the beautiful Southern Marsh Orchid. The latter will readily interbreed with similar orchid species to produce a hybrid swarm of individuals which may be highly variable and number many hundreds in favourable sites.

There are several other noteworthy smaller species of water meadow herb amongst which the aromatic Water Mint must be one of the most widespread. Usually catching the attention by its powerful fragrance of spearmint when crushed underfoot, it nevertheless produces dense heads of pale lilac flowers in the late summer. Other late flowerers include the Square Stemmed St. John's Wort and the Corky-Fruited Water Dropwort, whose abundance in Dorset is noted with envy by visiting botanists.

In ungrazed meadows, among the taller grasses and rushes may be found the larger herbaceous perennials. The bristly Comfrey with its cymes of many-hued, bee enticing tubular flowers, and the plentiful Yellow Flag Iris are amongst the earlier species to reach flowering height. They are followed, a month or so later by the Meadowsweet, the owner of sickly sweet creamy flower clusters, the statuesque Marsh Thistle, the Hemp Agrimony, and Great Willowherb, whose dried and wind-blasted stems will last until the onset of the autumn gales.

Alongside the banks of rivers, and usually clambering over the attendant vegetation are three species of climber which are not strictly limited to streamsides, but show a marked preference for such a niche. These are the Woody Nightshade, a poisonous relative of the edible Tomato, the Tufted Vetch, with its narrow leaflets, twining tendrils and its erect columns of tiny lilac flowers, and lastly the Greater Bindweed whose white showy trumpets were amongst the favourites of the celebrated botanical illustrator Rev. W. Keble Martin.

Cliff and Undercliff

Few would deny that for its length, the Dorset coastline is amongst the most varied in Great Britain. Although the saltings of Poole and Christchurch Harbours, the sand ridges of Studland and the massive pebble rampart of the Chesil demand the attention of the botanist, the seaward margin of the county is largely dominated by cliffs.

The teeming, tourist-thronged beaches of Bournemouth are backed by cliffs of golden-yellow sandstone and are the home of many introduced species of plant of which the Hottentot Fig is amongst the most spectacular. This South African member of the Mesembryanthemum family is characterized by water storing succulent leaves and mauve, daisy-like flowers. In certain localities, such as at Flaghead Chine, the cliff may be carpeted with Furzes, Heathers and their attendant parasites the Dodders,

The Sea Campion *(Silene vulgaris ssp maritima)* is at home in many maritime habitats and is particularly familiar on the Kimmeridge shale.

all indicators of acid, heathland soils. The presence of these species highlights the fact that all of what is now Bournemouth and Canford Cliffs was once heathland, relict communities of which are now confined to such unimprovable sites. The deep pine-filled ravines, or chines, which punctuate the sandstone wall were once the home of the Lesser Twayblade Orchid, a northern species typical of the upland moors of Scotland and believed to have been introduced to Bournemouth as an accidental amongst pine seed. This species is recorded in the Rev. E. F. Linton's *Flora of Bournemouth* but it has not been seen for many a year.

The chalky spine of Purbeck reaches its easternmost extension in the gleaming cliffs of Handfast Point. Plants are able to find a toehold on the soft cliff faces above the reach of the battering waves, and the impressive Wild Cabbage (forbear of the familiar garden vegetable) is plentiful. This species is a biennial and it produces its tall spikes of yellow, four-petalled flowers in its second year. It is joined by the Red Spur Valerian, an introduced species that is favoured by many insects which are attracted by its ready supply of sugary nectar. The tall Mignonette, known as Dyer's Rocket or Weld is also found on the chalk cliffs, whilst Cliff Top grassland is the home of a collection of Wild Carrot plants which appear to be intermediate between the maritime and the inland sub-species.

To the south of Swanage, the cliffs running east from Durlston Head are composed of Purbeck limestones and have in the past been quarried extensively, most notably at Tilly Whim and again at Seacombe and Winspit. Among the cracks in the limestone, the aromatic Rock Samphire may be found; this fleshy-leaved, greenish-flowered umbellifer is amongst the most typical of cliff-dwelling species and is often joined by the Stalked Scurvy Grass. On certain cliff-edges, the May blooming Early Spider Orchid may be found. This extremely local species is restricted to the Purbeck limestones, often only inches from the cliff-edge. Even rarer is the Carrot Broomrape, a total parasite of Wild Carrots and completely dependent upon its host for all its nutritional and energy requirements.

Kimmeridge Bay is ringed by cliffs of soapy shales, the lower levels of which yield valuable oil. The steep black cliffs are carpeted with tumbling clumps of white-flowered Sea Campion, a species which is equally at home on the shingle of the Chesil. Alongside the Campion are Wild Cabbages, aged Curled Docks with massive tap roots and spiny headed Teasels – much loved by butterflies and florists. Here too may grow the yellow flowered Bristly Ox-Tongue; the aerial parts of this plant are clothed with anchor-shaped hairs, a feature only encountered in the genus *Picris*.

The Purbeck limestones make a spectacular reappearance at Gad Cliff, but westward of Worbarrow Bay they form only a fringing remnant which has been pierced by the incessant barrage of the waves at Lulworth Cove and again at the magnificent natural arch of Durdle Door. Cliff vegetation on the chalk cliffs of Bat's Head includes the Rock Sea Lavender and the roughly-hairy Viper's Bugloss whose rich blue flowers are attractive to foraging bumble bees.

Beneath the massive chalk countenance of White Nothe, among the jumbled rubble of the undercliff, a highly characteristic flora has developed. In stable areas, scrubby thickets of Blackthorn, Hawthorn, Wayfaring Tree and Wild Privet grow, and these may be overlaid with twining Honeysuckle, rasping Madder and glossy-green Ivy, while more open communities boast many of the species typical of inland chalk grasslands.

Mirey flushes created by ground water seepage encourage the growth of tall Reeds and Rushes and a wealth of other moisture demanding species. The yellow flowered Coltsfoot is the first to show, putting up its flowers in late March to be followed in late spring by its large, down-covered leaves. Later in the year, a selection of Horsetails thrusts up through the soil, and these are often joined by the Gipsywort, and the autumn flowering Fleabane. Suitable sites may display a range of Southern Marsh Orchids, whose purple spikes may be found in considerable abundance in June, whilst July sees the Marsh Helleborine offering its creamy-yellow flowers to bee visitors. There are several areas below White Nothe where the undercliff supports wetland species and similar conditions are also encountered below St. Aldhelm's and on the D.N.T. reserve at Black Ven and the Spittles in the extreme west of the county.

The cliffs of Portland are richer in species than the limestone cliffs of Purbeck and one should find the diminutive Portland Spurge in abundance. This species is found on the mainland cliffs too, whilst the Portland Rock Sea-Lavender has a small endemic population on the island and is unknown elsewhere. The Cottonweed, always an extreme rarity in Dorset (and now apparently extinct) had its last recorded station near Weston whereas the Sea Spleenwort, a small maritime fern, still grows in cliff crevices in western Portland. The path-traversed undercliffs of Church Ope are a paradise for botanists, with Ivy Broomrape, rare Salad Cresses and Three-Fingered Saxifrages adding spice to an already diverse limestone flora.

The grassy base of the towering, sandstone crowned Golden Cap is devoid of species of note but the unstable lias and clay formations of Black Ven and the Spittles between Charmouth and Lyme are notable for the richness of their floras. The treacherous undercliffs are dotted with scrub species, but here and there, where the grass and scrub are less well-developed, Kidney Vetch and hundreds of Bee Orchids may flourish.

Cliff vegetation is relatively safe from loss through development but many species will only grow in this niche, and small isolated populations are always at risk. It is hoped that the more general awareness of the need for conservation should ensure the continued survival of the cliff flora.

The Coltsfoot favours damp localities on undercliffs.

Sand Dune and Shingle Bank

There are two highly individual plant communities which occur locally only within their restricted habitat formations. A sand dune flora has developed on the advancing series of wind-blown sand ridges which form the Studland dune complex; and the landward side of the majestic Chesil Bank affords an anchorage for the unusual assemblage of plants which colonises shingle.

Seventeenth and eighteenth century smugglers would hardly recognise the South Haven peninsular today, so dramatic have been the physical changes to the land over the past three centuries. Old county maps show no hint of the expanse of water known as the Little Sea and this feature is not recorded until 1721

A common species of Chalk downland, the Kidney Vetch *(Anthyllis vulneraria)* is equally at home on the pebble bank.

when a salt water lagoon (similar to the Fleet) first makes an appearance. During the last century the Studland Bay sand dunes consolidated their position and over the last eighty years have marched inexorably eastward.

Dry sand particles are moved along by the wind until they meet some irregularity in the surface over which they are being blown. They will then fall into the lee of this obstacle from where they can be moved no further. This action leads to the formation of miniature ridges at right angles to the prevailing wind.

Plants that colonise the strand or drift line (the area just above the reaches of the high spring tides and usually decorated with beached seaweeds) can act as the first of a series of traps to finely blown sand. When present, these pioneers form open communities which include the prickly and unattractive Saltwort and a variety of Orache species and the lilac flowered crucifer Sea Rocket. All these drift-line colonisers are annuals, and although they may capture small quantities of sand, these miniature hummocks will be dispersed when the plants die and the autumnal gales buffet the beach. The strand line assemblage is not strongly represented on beaches such as Studland which form a significant recreation area during the months of high summer.

These ridges of slightly drier sand which develop around the primary colonisers or over the tangle of seaweeds and kelps that litter the high water mark act as a suitable nursery bed for tougher maritime grasses which include the Lyme Grass, and the Sea Couch Grass. These two rhizomatous perennial species have a limited ability to grow through a pile of wind blown sand, and so they can cope with greater inundation than their less robust seaward precursors.

This ability to grow through sand is far surpassed by the rugged Marram Grass; a species ideally suited to cope with the rigours of water shortage, harsh drying winds and shifting sands. Marram can build dunes up to twenty metres in height and it can force its way through a metre of entombing sand each year. The leaves of this remarkable species roll inwards during dry weather, and so limit water loss through the leaf's upper surface, and present only the waxy lower surface to the dehydrating embrace of the wind.

The sand ensnared by the Marram is less prone to further dispersal, and the smaller Red Fescue Grass can gain a hold alongside the triangular stemmed Sand Sedge. This maritime Sedge grows in a distinctive fashion: evenly spaced and in straight lines across the sand. Close examination will reveal that the individual plants are linked by an underground stem system that roots at every node but only produces an aerial shoot at every fourth node. These two species serve to bind the dune surface together with a tightly interwoven mesh of rhizomes and roots.

It is here among the developing turf of the fixed dune that one can find another group of plants that are adapted to life in a region of distinct paucity of water. These are the so-called 'Winter Annuals': plants that germinate during the winter, and grow rapidly, encouraged by the ready supply of water present at that season. Amongst their number one should note the Little Mouse-Eared Chickweed and the Poor Man's Weatherglass, otherwise known as the Scarlet Pimpernel.

The landward edges of the dune system are invaded by a selection of ericaceous dwarf shrubs from the adjacent heathland: Ling on the drier sites, and the rose-pink flowered Cross Leaved Heath where the winter moisture remains longest.

Despite the fact that the Studland dune system is under pressure from leisure seekers who create a myriad of eroding pathways through the sand-hills the area as a whole is safe. Happily it is protected from development by the Nature Conservancy Council

51

The Creeping Cinquefoil
(Potentilla reptans) spreads by
runners like the garden
strawberry.

who administer the site as a National Nature Reserve.

In the Chesil Beach, Dorset is blessed with one of the three outstanding shingle features in Great Britain, and it has even been described as 'probably the most extensive and extraordinary accumulation of shingle in the world'. The great pebble bank extends from Burton Bradstock in a graceful curve some fifteen miles to Chesilton on the Isle of Portland. Between Abbotsbury and Smallmouth, the bank is backed by the shallow, tidal lagoon of the Fleet, an important refuge for wintering wildfowl. At its broadest the bank is some two hundred metres in width and fourteen metres in height.

On the landward side of the beach, sparse patches of vegetation dot the pebbles. Plants can only gain a toehold in this hostile environment when the shingly substrate is no longer subjected to constant wave action. Perhaps the most notable of these colonizers is the Shrubby Sea Blite, an evergreen member of the Goosefoot family which may be found in abundance fringing the Fleet but is of local distribution within the country as a whole.

The white flowered Sea Campion, also native on cliffs, is another plentiful inhabitant of these sheltered locations, and it may be found growing in association with the familiar Thrift which can be so abundant as to turn large areas into a sea of waving pink in early June. Scattered amongst the Thrift may be the three leguminous species: the yellow-flowered Kidney Vetch (more usually encountered on Chalk Downland) and Birdsfoot

Trefoil, and also the more modest Rough Clover. These herbaceous members of the pea family have nitrogen-fixing bacteria living in association with their roots and enable them to survive when there is a shortage of available ground-water nitrates.

Shingle species, in common with many other maritime plants are often equipped with fleshy leaves as a device for storing water. This group includes the glossy-green Sea Beet and the sea-side form of the Curled Dock. The poisonous Woody Nightshade, a widely distributed rambler of hedgerow and scrub also has a coastal form which is both succulent and prostrate and may be located in one or two sites towards the northern and western end of the bank, and again near Smallmouth.

The rough, deep rooted Yellow Horned Poppy is a frequent inhabitant of the pebbles in the Bexington to Abbotsbury section of the Bank and may be joined by the glorious purple-blue blossoms of the July flowering Sea Pea, whilst the Sea Holly, an unusual, spiny umbellifer with a domed head of bluish flowers is a much less common sight.

Vegetated shingle is a scarce habitat nationally and one that is at its delightful best during the later months of the summer when inland localities may offer little of interest to the botanist.

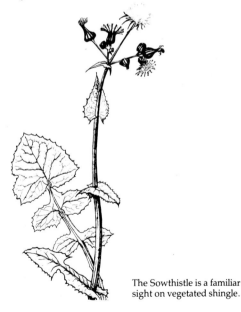

The Sowthistle is a familiar sight on vegetated shingle.

Saltmarsh

Saltmarsh as a habitat is scarce in Dorset, with the only significant expanses being found around the fringes of Poole and Christchurch Harbours and at Smallmouth, where the tidal Fleet runs into Portland Harbour. Areas now occurring within the Radipole Lake nature reserve were originally saltmarsh until the building of the Westham Bridge in 1924 which prevented the daily ebb and flow of the tide.

Any plant that is to survive and grow under the harsh conditions imposed by an environment where the salinity levels of the waterlogged soils are high, requires special adaptations. These adaptations enable the plants to take in water against an apparent concentration gradient and then to hold on to it when growing in positions which are often exposed to the dehydrating influence of the wind.

Only one group of flowering plants, the Eelgrasses (*Zostera* spp.) are adapted to a completely marine existence, living in the intertidal regions amongst the more conspicuous green algae. These Eelgrass species are plentiful around the coast and two species are recorded from both Poole Harbour and from the Fleet. The Eelgrasses are all pollinated by water; the pollen grains being long and of the same density as the sea water. This will prevent them from either sinking to the bottom or floating to the surface away from the receptive female stigmas.

Above the neap high tide line mark begins the salt marsh proper – subject to inundation with brackish water by the high spring tides. On the lower reaches of the saltmarsh, growing on the bare mud, are the Glassworts, whose branched succulent stems turn a bright scarlet in the autumn, and the Cord Grass, a vigorously growing, rhizomatous hybrid which is widespread, especially on the extensive flats surrounding the Wareham Channel and the Arne peninsula.

As mud accumulates about the stems of the Glasswort and the level of the saltmarsh is raised above that of the intertidal flats, the dwarf Sea Meadow Grass (*Puccinellia maritima*) becomes the dominant feature of the vegetation. Dotted over the grass sward may be colonies of the Sea Aster; a fleshy stemmed, purple-rayed member of the daisy family, the rose flowered Sea Pink and its

A small creek on the grazed Saltmarsh at Stanpit, Christchurch Harbour. This creek would be inundated at high water.

The Sea Pink, or Thrift *(Armeria maritima)*, will flourish on cliffs, shingle or on grazed Saltmarsh.

close relative the Sea Lavender whose crispy blue-purple flowers may be seen on display once June is out.

On the upper reaches of the marsh, the *Puccinellia* is replaced by the roll-leaved Red Fescue grass, and it is in this niche that the tall, pale flowered Marsh Mallow may be found. The leaves and stems of this species are clothed in a dense, velvety covering of star shaped hairs; another means of preventing excessive water loss in this unfavourable environment.

Saltmarshes are often traversed by a network of shallow, muddy, tidal creeks which are lined along their upper edges by the grey-green leaved, shrubby Sea Purslane, whilst the muddy hollows which pock-mark grassy saltmarsh may be fringed with Sea Arrowgrass and Mud Rush. Areas where the natural vegetation is compressed by the passage of vehicles or walkers is often dominated by the diminutive Buck's Horn Plantain whilst its larger relative, the Sea Plantain may accompany the Sea Beet, the Celery Leaved Crowfoot and the Saltmarsh Water Dropwort on the highest regions of the marsh.

Saltmarsh is of considerable importance nationally as a winter refuge for wading birds as many species feed on the intertidal flats and roost on the lower reaches of the marsh. Pollution presents the only major threat to this habitat and man's increasing awareness of his responsibilities in this area are a cause for cautious optimism for its future.

55

Weeds and Aliens

The majority of plants covered in this guide come from habitats that have been affected by man to a greater or lesser extent, there are however, several groups which merit separate treatment. These are species which are almost exclusively to be found in sites created by man, and included here are the weeds of cornfield and disturbed ground, the long established introductions, escapes from cultivation and casual species which may survive in a locality for a season or two but have added few lasting contributions to the flora.

Fields farmed for cereal crops have traditionally provided a home for a colourful display of weed species. Perennials find establishment difficult in an environment that is mown, ploughed and harrowed yearly and so it is annuals that form the bulk of the plants that can flourish amongst the waving corn stems. Annuals invest their reproductive energy in producing vast numbers of tiny seeds that have the ability to lie dormant in the soil for many years and to germinate only when conditions for growth are suitable.

Agricultural progress has increased the purity of cereal seed, and this, coupled with the widespread spraying of herbicides have ensured that cornfield colonists are today considerably less abundant than in the past. Although the blood-red Common Poppies are a not infrequent sight in fields and along road verges, other species are markedly scarcer. Amongst these scarcer species are the rich deep blue Cornflower, never common, even in the 1890's and the impressive, straggling, purplish-flowered Corn Cockle. Early popular flower books note the abundance of this plant throughout Great Britain, a position which is sadly no longer the case today, and it has now almost totally disappeared from Dorset.

Many arable weeds show a marked liking for chalky soils, and of these, a number are still reasonably abundant, finding their way onto roadbanks and verges in addition to suitable field margin localities. Two Daisy-like species – the white rayed Scentless Mayweed and the golden Corn Marigold form single-species stands in favoured sites and may be accompanied by the Corn Gromwell, the scented Mignonettes and the moth attracting

The highly variable Shepherd's Purse is a persistent nuisance in gardens.

White Campion. Where this last species grows near to the closely related hedgerow Red Campion, delicate pink-flowered hybrids commonly occur. Under similar conditions of soil and disturbance, low growing species often flourish and these may include the closely related Fluellens, and the Lesser Toadflax which often grow cheek by jowl with the aromatically scented Wild Basil, and the trailing stemmed Lesser Bindweed whose pinkish-white flowers are a powerful attractant to foraging honey bees.

Town gardens, associated urban waste ground and disused railway lines (of which Dorset has many miles) have provided a veritable paradise for weeds. The major components of the flora of these niches are often regarded by the gardener and farmer alike as the most pernicious of scourges, and indeed, they may be, but if allowed to develop and flower they can produce a colourful show of pinks, purples and yellows throughout the summer. Creeping Thistles, stray Buddleias, Evening Primroses and showy Rose-Bay Willowherbs and also the introduced Mediterranean species, the Oxford Ragwort. This plant owed its spectacular spread in the mid-nineteenth century to a combination of light, parachute-like seeds and the proximity of the Oxford botanic gardens to the newly opened Great Western Railway. The seeds were wafted along in the draught caused by passing trains and rapidly became established throughout Great Britain – radiating away from Oxford along the developing rail network.

Road-building projects expose large areas of soil to colonising plants which will develop either from dormant seeds or from wind borne fruits. Poppies are often amongst the first species to appear and they will be joined by several species of unattractive Goosefoot, daisy-like Mayweeds and the small and highly variable Shepherd's Purse. The tall and stately yellow-flavoured Mullein is a frequent invader of these habitats whereas the spiny, poisonous exotic Thorn Apple with its white trumpet-like flowers is much scarcer. The wind dispersed brigade are represented by various composites and Willowherbs of which Sow Thistles are amongst the largest and most conspicuous.

Changes in farming practice have resulted in certain crop plants falling from favour and disappearing almost completely from the agricultural scene. These species may have escaped from cultivation and established themselves alongside native species in seemingly natural habitats. The Sainfoin, a tall leguminous herb blessed with the most appealing of pink flowers is a good example. Planted on the Crichel estate by the innovating Sturt family in the eighteenth century as a soil restorer and fodder crop, it can still be found today on road verges in the vicinity of its former centre of cultivation. The Flax, once so vital to the sail cloth industry of Bridport and the Lucerne have likewise been replaced with alternatives but the latter fulfilled another purpose in the hot summer of 1983 – as food for the larvae of the particularly abundant Clouded Yellow Butterfly.

Walls have long been used as convenient boundary markers, and these have traditionally been constructed of locally quarried sands and limestones, but since the last century the more readily available brick has been widely used. In addition to a wide range of mosses and encrusting lichens, several species of fern may find a hold of which the Rusty-Back and the Wall-Rue seem the most dependent. The former species can survive even severe drought, and will recover rapidly from dessication with the advent of rain. Other wall dwellers include the purplish Ivy Leaved Toadflax and the fleshy leaved Wall Pennywort, a species which prefers the moister west of the county and in east Dorset is confined to a few heavily shaded and extremely damp roadbanks.

Many species introduced as ornamentals have found their way out of their originally intended sites and will now happily grow in a variety of habitats. Escaped ornamentals include the colony-forming Winter Heliotrope, whose deliciously scented flowers emerge in the mid-winter months of December and January and adorn roadside verges. Another possible escape is the February flowering Spring Snowflake, one of Dorset's most illustrious rarities; this plant has its only Dorset station on a secluded streamside near Lyme Regis.

Casuals: those species introduced accidentally from foreign parts are always of uncertain occurrence and may include a tantalizing pot-pourri of exotics ranging from Coriander to White Melilot. These are most usually associated with port areas or such places as have access to the sea. They are usually annuals as few of them are hardy enough to withstand the rigours of an English winter.

The Oxford dictionary describes a weed as any species of 'Wild Herb springing up where it is not wanted'. Many plants are undoubtedly capable of such behaviour, but it must be remembered that even the most unassuming of herbs has a place in the natural system and that although we may have no use for them they may be of great importance to other, less domineering organisms.

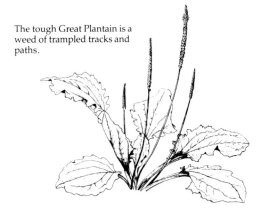

The tough Great Plantain is a weed of trampled tracks and paths.

Index of Species

61

63